VERBAL REASONING 1

PAPERS 1 – 4
(Multiple choice format)

Mary and Barbara Walsh M.A. (Oxon), P.G.C.E.

We would like to thank all our students, both past and present,
who have, often unwittingly, contributed to this book.

You know who you are and we dedicate this book to you.

ISBN (10 digit)   0-9553099-0-5
ISBN (13 digit)   978-0-9553099-0-8

Published by bumblebee (UK) Limited
Registered Office: 4 The Sanctuary, 23 Oakhill Grove, Surbiton, Surrey KT6 6DU

Paper 1

In the following questions, find **one** word from the top row and **one** word from the bottom row that will join together to form **one** correctly spelt new word.
The order of the letters does not change.

The word from the top row always comes first.

Mark **both** words on the answer sheet.

Example

    (he   she   we)
    (am   at   are)

Answer

    he   at   (the word is **heat**)

QUESTION **1**

(sleep   lie   rest)
(rain   ice   snow)

QUESTION **2**

(cart   part   hear)
(take   ledge   ten)

QUESTION **3**

(par   bear   soak)
(lament   ring   king)

QUESTION **4**

(in   car   under)
(turn   front   vent)

QUESTION **5**

(know   all   ear)
(liar   ledge   sort)

QUESTION **6**

(part   pour   steer)
(take   table   ridge)

QUESTION **7**

(bat   near   bash)
(tell   ring   her)

In the following questions, take a letter from the first word and move it into the second word to form two new words.

All the other letters must stay in the same order and both new words must make sense.

Work out which letter moves and mark it on the answer sheet.

Example

    heart   camp

Answer

    r   (the two new words are **heat** and **cramp**)

QUESTION **8**

flame   lint

QUESTION **9**

ideal   clam

QUESTION **10**

beard   bow

QUESTION **11**

plush   stale

QUESTION **12**

rinse   gash

QUESTION **13**

witch   row

QUESTION **14**

pilot   plan

KEEP GOING

GO STRAIGHT ON

In these questions, letters represent numbers. Work out the answer to each sum, find its letter and mark it on the answer sheet.

Example

If   A=4   B=3   C=2   D=6   E=1

what is the answer to this sum **as a letter**?

$$(B \times A) \div C = [\ ?\ ]$$

Answer

D

QUESTION **15**

If   A=3   B=5   C=4   D=2   E=30

what is the answer to this sum **as a letter**?

$$(A \times B \times C) \div D = [\ ?\ ]$$

QUESTION **16**

If   A=5   B=6   C=3   D=2   E=4

what is the answer to this sum **as a letter**?

$$B + C - E = [\ ?\ ]$$

QUESTION **17**

If   A=6   B=4   C=3   D=5   E=12

what is the answer to this sum **as a letter**?

$$(A \times C) - E = [\ ?\ ]$$

QUESTION **18**

If   A=12   B=10   C=4   D=2   E=3

what is the answer to this sum **as a letter**?

$$(C \times D \times E) \div A = [\ ?\ ]$$

KEEP GOING

QUESTION **19**

If   A=3   B=5   C=9   D=15   E=6

what is the answer to this sum **as a letter**?

$$(D \div B) \times A = [\ ?\ ]$$

QUESTION **20**

If   A=2   B=6   C=4   D=0   E=3

what is the answer to this sum **as a letter**?

$$B - C + A = [\ ?\ ]$$

QUESTION **21**

If   A=3   B=6   C=9   D=12   E=5

what is the answer to this sum **as a letter**?

$$D \div B \times A = [\ ?\ ]$$

Read the following information, then work out the correct answer to the question and mark it on the answer sheet.

QUESTION **22**

On their birthdays last year, George got nine cards more than John who got three more than Haroun.
John got twice as many as Narisra who got four.
David had as many as Narisra.
Yasmin got two less than David.

Which of the following statements is true?

a. George received 18 cards.

b. 42 cards were sent to the children.

c. George received 9 cards.

d. John received 4 cards.

e. Haroun received 5 cards.

GO STRAIGHT ON

In each sentence there is a word of **four** letters hidden between the end of one word and the beginning of the next.

Find the pair of words that contains the hidden word and mark your answer on the answer sheet.

Example

He skis so badly.

Answer

skis so (the hidden word is **kiss**)

QUESTION **23**

He ached from head to toe.

QUESTION **24**

Are you all going riding today?

QUESTION **25**

The picture over there is mine.

QUESTION **26**

Three men decided to go home.

QUESTION **27**

Mum agreed it was too dear.

QUESTION **28**

She showed her badge to us.

QUESTION **29**

There is dust under the chair.

QUESTION **30**

Tom baked her a chocolate cake.

KEEP GOING

In the following questions, three of the five words are related in some way.

Find the **two** words that do not go with these three and mark them **both** on the answer sheet.

Example

carrot   turnip   mango   pea   apple

Answer

mango   apple

QUESTION **31**

bellow   under   roar   shout   beneath

QUESTION **32**

guard   defend   attack   protect   assault

QUESTION **33**

demolish murder assassinate destroy wreck

QUESTION **34**

gift   accept   receive   present   get

QUESTION **35**

small   decade   century   minute   millennium

QUESTION **36**

secure   bind   taut   rigid   fasten

QUESTION **37**

enigma riddle solution answer outcome

GO STRAIGHT ON

Find **two** words, **one** from the top row and **one** from the bottom row, that are **closest in meaning**.

Mark **both** words on the answer sheet.

Example

(scent glass fragrant)
(bottle liquid odour)

Answer

scent   odour

QUESTION **38**

(originate imitate design)
(act mimic mime)

QUESTION **39**

(joyous mad happy)
(insane sad evil)

QUESTION **40**

(mend sew glue)
(damage exchange repair)

QUESTION **41**

(soak cool damp)
(moist flat dry)

QUESTION **42**

(scorn laugh praise)
(hate blush despise)

QUESTION **43**

(harsh cemetery serious)
(grave foolish stone)

QUESTION **44**

(seldom frequently rarely)
(never often always)

QUESTION **45**

(hinder behind aid)
(hunt impede destroy)

KEEP GOING

In the following questions, find the number that will complete the sum correctly and mark it on the answer sheet.

Example

$$8 \times 3 \div 2 = 5 \times 3 - [\,?\,]$$

Answer

3

QUESTION **46**

$$24 \div 2 + 4 = 30 - 6 - [\,?\,]$$

QUESTION **47**

$$(11 \times 4) \div 2 = 6 + 12 + [\,?\,]$$

QUESTION **48**

$$132 \div 12 = 3 \times 2 + [\,?\,]$$

QUESTION **49**

$$6 \times 4 \times 2 = 8 \times 8 - [\,?\,]$$

QUESTION **50**

$$(9 \div 3) \times 4 = 6 \times 4 \div [\,?\,]$$

QUESTION **51**

$$36 - 9 - 11 = 4 \times 2 \times [\,?\,]$$

QUESTION **52**

$$(25 + 15) \div 5 = 2 \times 2 \times [\,?\,]$$

GO STRAIGHT ON

7

Read the following information, then work out the correct answer to the question and mark it on the answer sheet.

QUESTION **53**

The red bus to town departs at 6.30 am.
The green bus to town departs at 6.15 am.
The green bus takes twice as long as the blue bus to cover the same route.
The blue bus leaves 15 minutes after the red bus and arrives in town at 7.30 am.

When does the green bus arrive in town?

a. 7.15 am.

b. 7.00 am.

c. 7.30 am.

d. 7.45 am.

e. 8.00 am.

KEEP GOING

In each of the following sentences, **three letters next to each other** have been removed from the word in capitals. These three letters make one correctly spelt word without changing their order. Find the missing three letter word and mark it on the answer sheet. The sentence must make sense.

Example

The cock **CED** loudly every morning.

Answer

ROW (The word in capitals is **CROWED**)

QUESTION **54**

CSON is my favourite colour.

QUESTION **55**

This clock **CES** every hour.

QUESTION **56**

It is dangerous to play **TRU** from school.

QUESTION **57**

There were **SEVL** biscuits on the plate.

QUESTION **58**

What is the **SCE** of your information?

QUESTION **59**

The lady renewed her television **LNCE**.

QUESTION **60**

The crowd's **REION** was one of joy.

GO STRAIGHT ON

Each question below contains three pairs of words. Find the word that completes the last pair of words in the **same way** as the other two pairs.
Mark your answer on the answer sheet.

Example

(three   the)   (shame   she)
(bacon   [?   ])

Answer   ban

QUESTION **61**

(deaden   need)   (dollar   road)
(mended   [?   ])

QUESTION **62**

(tracker   rack)   (feared   dear)
(locked   [?   ])

QUESTION **63**

(hid   hide)   (fox   foxy)
(bus   [?   ])

QUESTION **64**

(demean   mead)   (tidier   diet)
(temper   [?   ])

QUESTION **65**

(brainier   rain)   (unopened   none)
(flamenco   [?   ])

QUESTION **66**

(puddle   paddle)   (sour   soar)
(ruin   [?   ])

QUESTION **67**

(occult   cut)   (jeerer   err)
(astray   [?   ])

KEEP GOING

A B C D E F G H I J K L M N O P Q R S T U V W X Y Z

The alphabet is here to help you with the following questions.

Work out which pair of letters will come next in the series and mark your answer on the answer sheet.

Example

LX   MW   NV   OU   [?   ]

Answer

PT

QUESTION **68**

LY   OV   RS   UP   XM   [?   ]

QUESTION **69**

CU   ES   HP   LL   QG   [?   ]

QUESTION **70**

MZ   OX   RU   TS   WP   [?   ]

QUESTION **71**

AB   DE   HI   MN   ST   [?   ]

QUESTION **72**

FJ   GI   HH   IG   JF   [?   ]

QUESTION **73**

EU   GS   JP   NL   SG   [?   ]

QUESTION **74**

PA   QC   SD   TF   VG   [?   ]

GO STRAIGHT ON

Three of these four words are written in number code.

The codes are **not** written in the same order as the words and one of the codes is missing.

STAB   FAST   FITS   BAIT

5621   5312   1234

Work out the correct code for each word and answer the following questions.

Mark the correct answer on the answer sheet.

QUESTION **75**

Which word has the number code **5312**?

QUESTION **76**

What is the code for the word **BAIT**?

QUESTION **77**

What is the code for the word **SIFT**?

KEEP GOING

Three of these four words are written in number code.

The codes are **not** written in the same order as the words and one of the codes is missing.

HILL   HEEL   HIKE   LOOK

3665   1443   1233

Work out the correct code for each word and answer the following questions.

Mark the correct answer on the answer sheet.

QUESTION **78**

Which word has the number code **3665**?

QUESTION **79**

What is the code for the word **HIKE**?

QUESTION **80**

What is the code for the word **HELL**?

END OF TEST 1

Paper 2

In these questions, find a letter that will complete the word in front of the brackets and begin the word after the brackets. You must use the **same** letter in **both** sets of brackets.

Example

tra   (?)   et
man   (?)   es

Answer

y   (the four words are **tray, yet, many, yes**)

QUESTION **1**

tu   (?)   oat
wi   (?)   ull

QUESTION **2**

mo   (?)   asp
pa   (?)   eight

QUESTION **3**

drea   (?)   ock
clai   (?)   ean

QUESTION **4**

sti   (?)   ot
tie   (?)   est

QUESTION **5**

dra   (?)   ill
ro   (?)   lue

QUESTION **6**

sno   (?)   ear
ho   (?)   e

QUESTION **7**

hea   (?)   one
me   (?)   rain

KEEP GOING

In the following questions, take a letter from the first word and move it into the second word to form two new words. All the other letters must stay in the same order and both new words must make sense.

Work out which letter moves and mark it on the answer sheet.

Example

heart   camp

Answer

r   (the two new words are **heat** and **cramp**)

QUESTION **8**

bland   stale

QUESTION **9**

mince   rack

QUESTION **10**

blame   are

QUESTION **11**

raise   bet

QUESTION **12**

pleat   sit

QUESTION **13**

twine   pot

QUESTION **14**

cramp   fare

GO STRAIGHT ON

12

A B C D E F G H I J K L M N O P Q R S T U V W X Y Z

The alphabet is here to help you with the following questions. Work out which pair of letters will come next in the sequence and mark your answer on the answer sheet.

Example

    AZ is to **BY**
as
    CX is to [?]

Answer

    DW

QUESTION **15**

CR is to **AV**
as
FE is to [?]

QUESTION **16**

DE is to **GC**
as
HR is to [?]

QUESTION **17**

FS is to **KW**
as
MI is to [?]

QUESTION **18**

KK is to **LJ**
as
BB is to [?]

QUESTION **19**

HE is to **CE**
as
VA is to [?]

KEEP GOING

QUESTION **20**

ZA is to **AX**
as
YB is to [?]

QUESTION **21**

DM is to **CL**
as
XQ is to [?]

Read the information below and work out which statement is true. Mark its letter on the answer sheet.

QUESTION **22**

Indhu and Sinthya are twins.
Indhu was born eight years ago.
Tom is five years older than Sinthya.
Next year, Sahib will be half as old as Tom.
Asim was seven three years ago.

A. Sinthya is 7.

B. Tom is 12.

C. Sahib is 5.

D. Asim is 9.

E. Sahib is 6.

GO STRAIGHT ON

13

In the following questions, find **two** words, one from each row, that are **most opposite in meaning.**

Example

(borrow   buy   sell)
(purchase   own   lend)

Answer

borrow   lend

QUESTION **23**

(near   ascent   absent)
(gift   present   away)

QUESTION **24**

(voluntary   speak   demand)
(solitary   need   compulsory)

QUESTION **25**

(trivial   eager   request)
(keen   reluctant   ask)

QUESTION **26**

(simple   poor   wealthy)
(impoverished   kind   malevolent)

QUESTION **27**

(commence   commerce   content)
(commit   start   cease)

QUESTION **28**

(remove   demolish   deteriorate)
(improve   spoil   ruin)

QUESTION **29**

(folly   insane   happy)
(foolish   wisdom   jolly)

QUESTION **30**

(mean   fragile   extravagant)
(useful   hopeful   frugal)

KEEP GOING

In the following series, find the number which comes next in the most sensible way, and mark it on the answer sheet.

Example

1   3   5   7   [?]

Answer

9

QUESTION **31**

1   4   9   16   25   [?]

QUESTION **32**

1   2   3   5   8   13   [?]

QUESTION **33**

3   5   8   10   13   15   [?]

QUESTION **34**

64   16   4   [?]

QUESTION **35**

18   19   21   24   28   [?]

QUESTION **36**

2   2   4   12   48   [?]

QUESTION **37**

81   64   49   36   [?]

GO STRAIGHT ON

14

In each sentence there is a word of **four** letters hidden between the end of one word and the beginning of the next.

Find the pair of words that contains the hidden word and mark your answer on the answer sheet.

Example

He skis so badly.

Answer

skis so (the hidden word is **kiss**)

QUESTION **38**

That flower has very pretty petals.

QUESTION **39**

The boxer anticipated every little move.

QUESTION **40**

The foreman yelled at the carpenter.

QUESTION **41**

You will find his office downstairs.

QUESTION **42**

Each entrance is guarded by sentries.

QUESTION **43**

Her hair is long and red.

QUESTION **44**

Is the party really over now?

KEEP GOING

Read the following information, then work out the correct answer to the question and mark it on the answer sheet.

QUESTION **45**

There were twice as many girls as boys in the class.
One third of the girls had red hair.
There were twelve boys.

How many girls did not have red hair?

a. 8

b. 16

c. 4

d. 6

e. 12

In each of the following questions, there is the same relationship between the word outside the brackets and a word inside each set of brackets.
Choose **two** words, one from each set of brackets, that complete the sentence in the best way.

Example

cat is to
(tiger   kitten   calf)

as **dog** is to
(bone   kennel   puppy)

Answer

kitten   puppy

QUESTION **46**

placate is to
(plague   pacify   locate)

as **irritate** is to
(scratch   boil   annoy)

KEEP GOING

15

QUESTION **47**

coffee is to
(drink   bean   flavour)

as **tea** is to
(India   cup   leaf)

QUESTION **48**

drought is to
(damp   water   cold)

as **famine** is to
(farm   hunger   food)

QUESTION **49**

sunrise is to
(early   dawn   awake)

as **sunset** is to
(orange   dark   dusk)

QUESTION **50**

chair is to
(sleep   cushion   sit)

as **bed** is to
(table   lie   doze)

QUESTION **51**

building is to
(bricks   offices   foundations)

as **tree** is to
(roots   birds   branches)

QUESTION **52**

watch is to
(clock   time   see)

as **compass** is to
(needle   direction   west)

GO STRAIGHT ON

A B C D E F G H I J K L M N O P Q R S T U V W X Y Z

The alphabet is here to help you with the following questions. There is a different code for each question. Find the correct answer and mark it on the answer sheet.

Example

If the code for **HARD** is **IBSE,** what does **UFTU** mean?

Answer   **TEST**

QUESTION **53**

If the code for **CREAM** is **FPHYP,** what is the code for **MILKY**?

QUESTION **54**

If the code for **SHARP** is **UKEUR,** what does **RRMQV** mean?

QUESTION **55**

If the code for **FLOOR** is **GNRSW,** what is the code for **TILES**?

QUESTION **56**

If the code for **OPEN** is **LLZH,** what does **PDPN** mean?

QUESTION **57**

If the code for **LAMP** is **QEPR,** what is the code for **POST**?

QUESTION **58**

If the code for **BLOT** is **YOLG,** what does **KZTV** mean?

QUESTION **59**

If the code for **SNAKE** is **QKWFY,** what is the code for **VIPER**?

GO STRAIGHT ON

In each question there are two pairs of words.
Only **one** of the answers will go equally
well with **both** pairs of words.
Mark **one** word on the answer sheet.

Example

(just   reasonable)
(blonde   light)

Answer

fair

QUESTION **60**

(govern   reign)
(draw   delineate)

QUESTION **61**

(fee   rate)
(advance   attack)

QUESTION **62**

(design   paint)
(tug   pull)

QUESTION **63**

(competition   tournament)
(oppose   object)

QUESTION **64**

(stumble   fall)
(excursion journey)

QUESTION **65**

(hurry   hasten)
(line   hyphen)

QUESTION **66**

(tulips   roses)
(flourishes blossoms)

KEEP GOING

In the following questions, the three numbers
in **each** group are related in the **same** way.

Find the number which belongs with the last
group and mark it on the answer sheet.

Example

(2 [6] 3)   (4 [8] 2)

(5 [?] 3)

Answer

15

QUESTION **67**

(16 [9] 8)   (15 [7] 9)

(14 [?] 10)

QUESTION **68**

(3 [30] 9)   (5 [50] 9)

(6 [?] 8)

QUESTION **69**

(12 [20] 4)   (8 [26] 9)

(6 [?] 7)

QUESTION **70**

(11 [132] 12)   (12 [108] 9)

(15 [?] 6)

QUESTION **71**

(24 [47] 2)   (13 [38] 3)

(12 [?] 7)

GO STRAIGHT ON

QUESTION **72**

(9 [11] 13) (22 [24] 26)

(31 [?] 35)

QUESTION **73**

(6 [14] 4) (10 [26] 8)

(14 [?] 10)

QUESTION **74**

(10 [40] 100) (5 [35] 80)

(15 [?] 60)

KEEP GOING

Each question below contains three pairs of words.

Find the word that completes the last pair of words in the **same way** as the other two pairs.

Mark your answer on the answer sheet.

Example

(three the) (shame she)
(bacon [?])

Answer

ban

QUESTION **75**

(call calm) (pall palm)
(ball [?])

QUESTION **76**

(attempt team) (absorbs soar)
(acronym [?])

QUESTION **77**

(mass mess) (sell sill)
(firm [?])

QUESTION **78**

(err merry) (one money)
(eat [?])

QUESTION **79**

(sashes ash) (barter art)
(gunner [?])

QUESTION **80**

(barren bran) (follow flow)
(stable [?])

END OF TEST 2

MULTIPLE CHOICE ANSWER SHEET 1

**Please mark your answers with a single line
from side to side across the box ▭**

Do not mark outside the boxes

EXAMPLE

he ▬	am ☐
she ☐	at ▬
we ☐	are ☐

1

sleep ☐	rain ☐
lie ☐	ice ☐
rest ☐	snow ☐

2

cart ☐	take ☐
part ☐	ledge ☐
hear ☐	ten ☐

3

par ☐	lament ☐
bear ☐	ring ☐
soak ☐	king ☐

4

in ☐	turn ☐
car ☐	front ☐
under ☐	vent ☐

5

know ☐	liar ☐
all ☐	ledge ☐
ear ☐	sort ☐

6

part ☐	take ☐
pour ☐	table ☐
steer ☐	ridge ☐

7

bat ☐	tell ☐
near ☐	ring ☐
bash ☐	her ☐

EXAMPLE

| h ☐ |
| e ☐ |
| a ☐ |
| r ▬ |
| t ☐ |

8

| f ☐ |
| l ☐ |
| a ☐ |
| m ☐ |
| e ☐ |

9

| i ☐ |
| d ☐ |
| e ☐ |
| a ☐ |
| l ☐ |

10

| b ☐ |
| e ☐ |
| a ☐ |
| r ☐ |
| d ☐ |

11

| p ☐ |
| l ☐ |
| u ☐ |
| s ☐ |
| h ☐ |

12

| r ☐ |
| i ☐ |
| n ☐ |
| s ☐ |
| e ☐ |

13

| w ☐ |
| i ☐ |
| t ☐ |
| c ☐ |
| h ☐ |

14

| p ☐ |
| i ☐ |
| l ☐ |
| o ☐ |
| t ☐ |

EXAMPLE

| A ☐ |
| B ☐ |
| C ☐ |
| D ▬ |
| E ☐ |

15

| A ☐ |
| B ☐ |
| C ☐ |
| D ☐ |
| E ☐ |

16

| A ☐ |
| B ☐ |
| C ☐ |
| D ☐ |
| E ☐ |

17

| A ☐ |
| B ☐ |
| C ☐ |
| D ☐ |
| E ☐ |

18

| A ☐ |
| B ☐ |
| C ☐ |
| D ☐ |
| E ☐ |

19

| A ☐ |
| B ☐ |
| C ☐ |
| D ☐ |
| E ☐ |

20

| A ☐ |
| B ☐ |
| C ☐ |
| D ☐ |
| E ☐ |

21

| A ☐ |
| B ☐ |
| C ☐ |
| D ☐ |
| E ☐ |

22

| a ☐ |
| b ☐ |
| c ☐ |
| d ☐ |
| e ☐ |

EXAMPLE

| He skis ☐ |
| skis so ▬ |
| so badly. ☐ |

23

| He ached ☐ |
| ached from ☐ |
| from head ☐ |
| head to ☐ |
| to toe. ☐ |

24

| Are you ☐ |
| you all ☐ |
| all going ☐ |
| going riding ☐ |
| riding today? ☐ |

25

| The picture ☐ |
| picture over ☐ |
| over there ☐ |
| there is ☐ |
| is mine. ☐ |

26

| Three men ☐ |
| men decided ☐ |
| decided to ☐ |
| to go ☐ |
| go home. ☐ |

27

| Mum agreed ☐ |
| agreed it ☐ |
| it was ☐ |
| was too ☐ |
| too dear. ☐ |

28

| She showed ☐ |
| showed her ☐ |
| her badge ☐ |
| badge to ☐ |
| to us. ☐ |

29

| There is ☐ |
| is dust ☐ |
| dust under ☐ |
| under the ☐ |
| the chair. ☐ |

30

| Tom baked ☐ |
| baked her ☐ |
| her a ☐ |
| a chocolate ☐ |
| chocolate cake. ☐ |

EXAMPLE

| carrot ☐ |
| turnip ☐ |
| mango ▬ |
| pea ☐ |
| apple ▬ |

31

| bellow ☐ |
| under ☐ |
| roar ☐ |
| shout ☐ |
| beneath ☐ |

32

| guard ☐ |
| defend ☐ |
| attack ☐ |
| protect ☐ |
| assault ☐ |

33

| demolish ☐ |
| murder ☐ |
| assassinate ☐ |
| destroy ☐ |
| wreck ☐ |

34

| gift ☐ |
| accept ☐ |
| receive ☐ |
| present ☐ |
| get ☐ |

35

| small ☐ |
| decade ☐ |
| century ☐ |
| minute ☐ |
| millennium ☐ |

36

| secure ☐ |
| bind ☐ |
| taut ☐ |
| rigid ☐ |
| fasten ☐ |

37

| enigma ☐ |
| riddle ☐ |
| solution ☐ |
| answer ☐ |
| outcome ☐ |

PLEASE TURN OVER THE PAGE

EXAMPLE

scent	▭=	bottle	▭
glass	▭	liquid	▭
fragrant	▭	odour	▭=

38

originate	▭	act	▭
imitate	▭	mimic	▭
design	▭	mime	▭

39

joyous	▭	insane	▭
mad	▭	sad	▭
happy	▭	evil	▭

40

mend	▭	damage	▭
sew	▭	exchange	▭
glue	▭	repair	▭

41

soak	▭	moist	▭
cool	▭	flat	▭
damp	▭	dry	▭

42

scorn	▭	hate	▭
laugh	▭	blush	▭
praise	▭	despise	▭

43

harsh	▭	grave	▭
cemetery	▭	foolish	▭
serious	▭	stone	▭

44

seldom	▭	never	▭
frequently	▭	always	▭
rarely	▭	often	▭

45

hinder	▭	hunt	▭
behind	▭	impede	▭
aid	▭	destroy	▭

EXAMPLE

1	▭
2	▭
3	▭=
4	▭
5	▭

46

6	▭
8	▭
9	▭
10	▭
12	▭

47

2	▭
4	▭
6	▭
8	▭
10	▭

48

4	▭
5	▭
6	▭
7	▭
8	▭

49

12	▭
14	▭
16	▭
18	▭
20	▭

50

2	▭
3	▭
4	▭
5	▭
6	▭

51

1	▭
2	▭
3	▭
4	▭
5	▭

52

0	▭
1	▭
2	▭
3	▭
4	▭

53

a	
b	
c	
d	
e	

EXAMPLE

HER	▭
ROW	▭=
HIM	▭
RAT	▭
LOW	▭

54

ASS	▭
HOT	▭
HIM	▭
RIM	▭
APT	▭

55

ROW	▭
ALL	▭
HIM	▭
ERA	▭
ART	▭

56

MAN	▭
ANT	▭
GET	▭
GOT	▭
PET	▭

57

ARE	▭
ERA	▭
EVE	▭
ILL	▭
AIL	▭

58

ARC	▭
CAR	▭
OUR	▭
EAR	▭
ARE	▭

59

ACE	▭
ICE	▭
ACT	▭
EAR	▭
OIL	▭

60

LEG	▭
AIR	▭
CAR	▭
ART	▭
ACT	▭

EXAMPLE

can	▭
con	▭
cob	▭
ban	▭=
cab	▭

61

mend	▭
deed	▭
need	▭
deem	▭
dene	▭

62

dole	▭
cold	▭
deck	▭
lock	▭
dock	▭

63

buss	▭
busy	▭
bush	▭
busk	▭
bust	▭

64

meet	▭
mere	▭
peer	▭
pert	▭
tree	▭

65

name	▭
came	▭
lame	▭
lane	▭
lean	▭

66

rear	▭
roar	▭
rein	▭
rain	▭
roan	▭

67

ray	▭
rat	▭
sat	▭
sty	▭
try	▭

EXAMPLE

QT	▭
PT	▭=
QS	▭
OT	▭
OS	▭

68

AI	▭
ZI	▭
BJ	▭
AJ	▭
ZJ	▭

69

VA	▭
VZ	▭
WZ	▭
WA	▭
WB	▭

70

YO	▭
YN	▭
YM	▭
ZO	▭
ZM	▭

71

YZ	▭
YA	▭
ZA	▭
ZB	▭
ZZ	▭

72

EK	▭
EL	▭
KE	▭
KD	▭
LE	▭

73

YA	▭
YZ	▭
AY	▭
ZY	▭
AZ	▭

74

IX	▭
XI	▭
XH	▭
WH	▭
WI	▭

75

STAB	▭
FAST	▭
FITS	▭
BAIT	▭
FIST	▭

76

5621	▭
5312	▭
1234	▭
5612	▭
4362	▭

77

1234	▭
5312	▭
5612	▭
1652	▭
4621	▭

78

HILL	▭
HIKE	▭
HEEL	▭
LOOK	▭
LEEK	▭

79

3254	▭
3665	▭
1443	▭
1233	▭
1254	▭

80

3254	▭
3445	▭
1433	▭
1233	▭
1254	▭

END OF TEST 1

MULTIPLE CHOICE ANSWER SHEET 2

**Please mark your answers with a single line
from side to side across the box** ⊟

Do not mark outside the boxes

EXAMPLE
- m ☐
- t ☐
- ŋ ☐
- d ☐
- y ⊟

1
- b ☐
- d ☐
- g ☐
- m ☐
- n ☐

2
- b ☐
- p ☐
- h ☐
- d ☐
- w ☐

3
- d ☐
- l ☐
- r ☐
- m ☐
- w ☐

4
- p ☐
- d ☐
- r ☐
- g ☐
- l ☐

5
- w ☐
- m ☐
- g ☐
- b ☐
- f ☐

6
- d ☐
- g ☐
- p ☐
- t ⊟
- w ☐

7
- l ☐
- p ☐
- b ☐
- t ☐
- d ☐

EXAMPLE
- h ☐
- e ☐
- a ☐
- r ⊟
- t ☐

8
- b ☐
- l ☐
- a ☐
- n ☐
- d ☐

9
- m ☐
- i ☐
- n ☐
- c ☐
- e ☐

10
- b ☐
- l ☐
- a ☐
- m ☐
- e ☐

11
- r ☐
- a ☐
- i ☐
- s ☐
- e ☐

12
- p ☐
- l ☐
- e ☐
- a ☐
- t ☐

13
- t ☐
- w ☐
- i ☐
- n ☐
- e ☐

14
- c ☐
- r ☐
- a ☐
- m ☐
- p ☐

EXAMPLE
- WD ☐
- BW ☐
- BY ☐
- DW ⊟
- YB ☐

15
- DC ☐
- HJ ☐
- IH ☐
- ID ☐
- DI ☐

16
- JO ☐
- JK ☐
- KO ☐
- KP ☐
- KG ☐

17
- RL ☐
- SL ☐
- RM ☐
- SM ☐
- QL ☐

18
- CB ☐
- CD ☐
- CA ☐
- AD ☐
- AC ☐

19
- AA ☐
- QB ☐
- QA ☐
- AR ☐
- AQ ☐

20
- CY ☐
- ZY ☐
- ZA ☐
- ZB ☐
- YA ☐

21
- YO ☐
- WO ☐
- VO ☐
- VP ☐
- WP ☐

22
- A ☐
- B ☐
- C ☐
- D ☐
- E ☐

EXAMPLE
- borrow ⊟
- buy ☐
- sell ☐
- purchase ☐
- own ☐
- lend ⊟

23
- near ☐
- ascent ☐
- absent ☐
- gift ☐
- present ☐
- away ☐

24
- voluntary ☐
- speak ☐
- demand ☐
- solitary ☐
- need ☐
- compulsory ☐

25
- trivial ☐
- eager ☐
- request ☐
- keen ☐
- reluctant ☐
- ask ☐

26
- simple ☐
- poor ☐
- wealthy ☐
- kind ☐
- impoverished ☐
- malevolent ☐

27
- commence ☐
- commerce ☐
- content ☐
- commit ☐
- start ☐
- cease ☐

28
- remove ☐
- demolish ☐
- deteriorate ☐
- improve ☐
- spoil ☐
- ruin ☐

29
- folly ☐
- insane ☐
- happy ☐
- foolish ☐
- wisdom ☐
- jolly ☐

30
- mean ☐
- fragile ☐
- extravagant ☐
- useful ☐
- hopeful ☐
- frugal ☐

EXAMPLE
- 6 ☐
- 7 ☐
- 8 ☐
- 9 ⊟
- 10 ☐

31
- 34 ☐
- 35 ☐
- 36 ☐
- 37 ☐
- 38 ☐

32
- 18 ☐
- 19 ☐
- 20 ☐
- 21 ☐
- 22 ☐

33
- 17 ☐
- 18 ☐
- 19 ☐
- 20 ☐
- 21 ☐

34
- 0 ☐
- 1 ☐
- 2 ☐
- 3 ☐
- 4 ☐

35
- 29 ☐
- 30 ☐
- 31 ☐
- 32 ☐
- 33 ☐

36
- 96 ☐
- 120 ☐
- 232 ☐
- 240 ☐
- 280 ☐

37
- 16 ☐
- 18 ☐
- 25 ☐
- 27 ☐
- 30 ☐

PLEASE TURN OVER THE PAGE

EXAMPLE
- He skis ☐
- skis so ▭
- so badly. ☐

38
- That flower ☐
- flower has ☐
- has very ☐
- very pretty ☐
- pretty petals. ☐

39
- The boxer ☐
- boxer anticipated ☐
- anticipated every ☐
- every little ☐
- little move. ☐

40
- The foreman ☐
- foreman yelled ☐
- yelled at ☐
- at the ☐
- the carpenter. ☐

41
- You will ☐
- will find ☐
- find his ☐
- his office ☐
- office downstairs. ☐

42
- Each entrance ☐
- entrance is ☐
- is guarded ☐
- guarded by ☐
- by sentries. ☐

43
- Her hair ☐
- hair is ☐
- is long ☐
- long and ☐
- and red. ☐

44
- Is the ☐
- the party ☐
- party really ☐
- really over ☐
- over now? ☐

45
- a ☐
- b ☐
- c ☐
- d ☐
- e ☐

EXAMPLE
- tiger ☐ bone ☐
- kitten ▭ kennel ☐
- calf ☐ puppy ▭

46
- plague ☐ scratch ☐
- pacify ☐ boil ☐
- locate ☐ annoy ☐

47
- drink ☐ India ☐
- bean ☐ cup ☐
- flavour ☐ leaf ☐

48
- damp ☐ farm ☐
- water ☐ hunger ☐
- cold ☐ food ☐

49
- early ☐ orange ☐
- dawn ☐ dark ☐
- awake ☐ dusk ☐

50
- sleep ☐ table ☐
- cushion ☐ lie ☐
- sit ☐ doze ☐

51
- bricks ☐ roots ☐
- offices ☐ birds ☐
- foundations ☐ branches ☐

52
- clock ☐ needle ☐
- time ☐ direction ☐
- see ☐ west ☐

EXAMPLE
- WETS ☐
- VETS ☐
- VEST ☐
- TEST ▭
- WEST ☐

53
- JKIMV ☐
- JKOMV ☐
- JKIMU ☐
- PGOIB ☐
- PGOIA ☐

54
- TURNS ☐
- TUNDRA ☐
- TUMMY ☐
- POISE ☐
- POINT ☐

55
- SGIAN ☐
- SGIBN ☐
- ULPJY ☐
- UKOIX ☐
- UKMGU ☐

56
- SHIN ☐
- SHIP ☐
- SHUT ☐
- MALE ☐
- MAKE ☐

57
- TRUU ☐
- USVV ☐
- USWV ☐
- KKQR ☐
- KKPR ☐

58
- CAGE ☐
- RAGE ☐
- PAGE ☐
- PALE ☐
- PALM ☐

59
- UGLZL ☐
- TFMAM ☐
- TFLZL ☐
- XLTTJX ☐
- XLTTJW ☐

EXAMPLE
- fair ▭
- party ☐
- fete ☐
- festival ☐
- rave ☐

60
- lead ☐
- crown ☐
- delegate ☐
- rule ☐
- line ☐

61
- cost ☐
- wage ☐
- salary ☐
- amount ☐
- charge ☐

62
- draw ☐
- tow ☐
- make ☐
- adapt ☐
- tear ☐

63
- game ☐
- beat ☐
- match ☐
- contest ☐
- item ☐

64
- clumsy ☐
- coach ☐
- drive ☐
- holiday ☐
- trip ☐

65
- dash ☐
- spot ☐
- dot ☐
- blot ☐
- rush ☐

66
- grows ☐
- blooms ☐
- petals ☐
- bulbs ☐
- roots ☐

EXAMPLE
- 4 ☐
- 5 ☐
- 10 ☐
- 15 ▭
- 20 ☐

67
- 2 ☐
- 3 ☐
- 4 ☐
- 5 ☐
- 6 ☐

68
- 40 ☐
- 51 ☐
- 53 ☐
- 54 ☐
- 56 ☐

69
- 13 ☐
- 19 ☐
- 20 ☐
- 25 ☐
- 48 ☐

70
- 45 ☐
- 60 ☐
- 75 ☐
- 80 ☐
- 90 ☐

71
- 71 ☐
- 73 ☐
- 83 ☐
- 84 ☐
- 85 ☐

72
- 11 ☐
- 22 ☐
- 32 ☐
- 33 ☐
- 34 ☐

73
- 16 ☐
- 28 ☐
- 32 ☐
- 34 ☐
- 40 ☐

74
- 15 ☐
- 30 ☐
- 35 ☐
- 40 ☐
- 45 ☐

EXAMPLE
- can ☐
- con ☐
- cob ☐
- ban ▭
- cab ☐

75
- bite ☐
- bile ☐
- bald ☐
- balm ☐
- bale ☐

76
- corn ☐
- coma ☐
- many ☐
- roam ☐
- moan ☐

77
- harm ☐
- farm ☐
- form ☐
- fill ☐
- fuss ☐

78
- treaty ☐
- sweaty ☐
- meaty ☐
- breath ☐
- death ☐

79
- gnu ☐
- urn ☐
- gun ☐
- rug ☐
- nun ☐

80
- stab ☐
- seal ☐
- sale ☐
- seat ☐
- sate ☐

END OF TEST 2

MULTIPLE CHOICE ANSWER SHEET 3

Please mark your answers with a single line
from side to side across the box ⊟

Do not mark outside the boxes

EXAMPLE
- He skis ☐
- skis so ⊟
- so badly ☐

1
- There is ☐
- is hair ☐
- hair on ☐
- on your ☐
- your jacket. ☐

2
- He loves ☐
- loves his ☐
- his three ☐
- three white ☐
- white mice. ☐

3
- It was ☐
- was quiet ☐
- quiet in ☐
- in the ☐
- the village. ☐

4
- Make enough ☐
- enough cakes ☐
- cakes for ☐
- for us ☐
- us all! ☐

5
- Anna created ☐
- created an ☐
- an aromatic ☐
- aromatic herb ☐
- herb garden. ☐

6
- Our relatives ☐
- relatives are ☐
- are away ☐
- away this ☐
- this week. ☐

7
- Have you ☐
- you got ☐
- got your ☐
- your geometry ☐
- geometry set? ☐

EXAMPLE
- m ☐
- t ☐
- p ☐
- d ☐
- y ⊟

8
- t ☐
- b ☐
- g ☐
- p ☐
- d ☐

9
- p ☐
- n ☐
- s ☐
- t ☐
- c ☐

10
- b ☐
- w ☐
- g ☐
- p ☐
- s ☐

11
- o ☐
- d ☐
- e ☐
- b ☐
- g ☐

12
- a ☐
- e ☐
- i ☐
- o ☐
- u ☐

13
- d ☐
- s ☐
- o ☐
- t ☐
- e ☐

14
- t ☐
- w ☐
- y ☐
- b ☐
- m ☐

EXAMPLE
- A ☐
- B ☐
- C ☐
- D ⊟
- E ☐

15
- A ☐
- B ☐
- C ☐
- D ☐
- E ☐

16
- A ☐
- B ☐
- C ☐
- D ☐
- E ☐

17
- A ☐
- B ☐
- C ☐
- D ☐
- E ☐

18
- A ☐
- B ☐
- C ☐
- D ☐
- E ☐

19
- A ☐
- B ☐
- C ☐
- D ☐
- E ☐

20
- A ☐
- B ☐
- C ☐
- D ☐
- E ☐

21
- A ☐
- B ☐
- C ☐
- D ☐
- E ☐

22
- a ☐
- b ☐
- c ☐
- d ☐
- e ☐

EXAMPLE
- scent ⊟
- glass ☐
- fragrant ☐
- bottle ☐
- liquid ☐
- odour ⊟

23
- force ☐
- make ☐
- soldier ☐
- police ☐
- power ☐
- destroy ☐

24
- region ☐
- reign ☐
- ruler ☐
- diameter ☐
- line ☐
- area ☐

25
- play ☐
- toil ☐
- relax ☐
- football ☐
- idle ☐
- labour ☐

26
- own ☐
- mine ☐
- gift ☐
- take ☐
- possess ☐
- receive ☐

27
- freedom ☐
- captivity ☐
- prison ☐
- convict ☐
- lock ☐
- liberty ☐

28
- sure ☐
- uncertain ☐
- left ☐
- right ☐
- wrong ☐
- doubtful ☐

29
- cry ☐
- apologize ☐
- pardon ☐
- forgive ☐
- laugh ☐
- permit ☐

EXAMPLE
- HER ☐
- ROW ⊟
- HIM ☐
- RAT ☐
- LOW ☐

30
- ERA ☐
- SON ☐
- AGE ☐
- SUN ☐
- POT ☐

31
- TEN ☐
- TAN ☐
- IRE ☐
- TIN ☐
- TRY ☐

32
- LAY ☐
- EVE ☐
- TIE ☐
- AMP ☐
- ROW ☐

33
- EAT ☐
- EAR ☐
- RAT ☐
- BAR ☐
- RUT ☐

34
- ICE ☐
- EWE ☐
- ILL ☐
- OAK ☐
- TEA ☐

35
- SIN ☐
- AMP ☐
- USE ☐
- SON ☐
- IMP ☐

36
- ILL ☐
- SEA ☐
- ATE ☐
- EAT ☐
- ACT ☐

PLEASE TURN OVER THE PAGE

EXAMPLE		37		38		39		40		41		42		43	
can	☐	rue	☐	rend	☐	err	☐	mild	☐	beard	☐	coir	☐	lure	☐
con	☐	cut	☐	rand	☐	her	☐	mile	☐	bread	☐	core	☐	rule	☐
cob	☐	err	☐	rang	☐	wee	☐	mill	☐	bared	☐	clot	☐	true	☐
ban	▭	rut	☐	aged	☐	hew	☐	male	☐	breed	☐	coil	☐	lute	☐
cab	☐	sit	☐	rage	☐	ewe	☐	mall	☐	braid	☐	cite	☐	tell	☐

EXAMPLE				44				45				46				47			
he	▭	am	☐	cot	☐	rely	☐	past	☐	our	☐	ram	☐	sack	☐	sow	☐	apple	☐
she	☐	at	▭	since	☐	age	☐	hum	☐	try	☐	tomb	☐	tour	☐	reap	☐	plum	☐
we	☐	are	▭	fir	☐	try	☐	man	☐	edge	☐	crumb	☐	bled	☐	sew	☐	pear	☐

48				49				50				51			
comb	☐	pert	☐	at	☐	rate	☐	ran	☐	able	☐	mist	☐	are	☐
ram	☐	bat	☐	port	☐	tend	☐	time	☐	side	☐	pan	☐	near	☐
sup	☐	part	☐	dim	☐	some	☐	peas	☐	sack	☐	poet	☐	try	☐

EXAMPLE		52		53		54		55		56		57		58	
2	☐	4	☐	6	☐	1	☐	4	☐	19	☐	2	☐	3	☐
3	☐	5	☐	8	☐	3	☐	5	☐	20	☐	3	☐	4	☐
4	▭	6	☐	9	☐	5	☐	6	☐	21	☐	6	☐	6	☐
6	☐	7	☐	10	☐	6	☐	7	☐	33	☐	10	☐	8	☐
12	☐	8	☐	14	☐	15	☐	8	☐	35	☐	30	☐	12	☐

EXAMPLE		59		60		61		62	
carrot	☐	kite	☐	astonishment	☐	attain	☐	plateau	☐
turnip	☐	oval	☐	wander	☐	reach	☐	peak	☐
mango	▭	rectangle	☐	ramble	☐	buy	☐	top	☐
pea	☐	diamond	☐	wonder	☐	achieve	☐	level	☐
apple	▭	circle	☐	rove	☐	purchase	☐	summit	☐

63		64		65		66		67	
clock	☐	origin	☐	singe	☐	barometer	☐	a	☐
calendar	☐	terminus	☐	char	☐	ruler	☐	b	☐
hourglass	☐	end	☐	blow	☐	elements	☐	c	☐
watch	☐	finish	☐	burn	☐	weather	☐	d	☐
diary	☐	source	☐	puff	☐	thermometer	☐	e	☐

EXAMPLE		68		69		70		71		72		73	
QT	☐	DG	☐	DR	☐	FF	☐	FU	☐	ZV	☐	GU	☐
PT	▭	DF	☐	FS	☐	FF	▭	UF	☐	BV	☐	IIU	☐
QS	☐	EF	☐	FR	☐	FG	☐	TG	☐	AV	☐	UH	☐
OT	☐	EG	☐	DS	☐	EG	☐	TF	☐	AU	☐	UG	☐
OS	☐	EH	☐	DT	☐	GF	☐	UG	☐	AW	☐	UI	☐

74		75		76		77		78		79		80	
ZM	☐	SKIP	☐	1254	☐	4255	☐	DICE	☐	1432	☐	5412	☐
ZR	☐	SIFT	☐	1324	☐	6231	☐	TIDE	☐	1421	☐	1432	☐
BM	☐	SPIT	☐	1623	☐	1623	☐	TIED	☐	5421	☐	1425	☐
MA	☐	FIST	☐	6211	☐	1324	☐	EDIT	☐	4321	☐	3452	☐
AM	☐	KISS	☐	1624	☐	5214	☐	DIET	☐	3452	☐	1421	☐

END OF TEST 3

MULTIPLE CHOICE ANSWER SHEET 4

**Please mark your answers with a single line
from side to side across the box** ▭

Do not mark outside the boxes

EXAMPLE
- h ▭
- e ▭
- a ▭
- r ▬
- t ▭

1
- f ▭
- o ▭
- u ▭
- n ▭
- d

2
- t ▭
- e ▭
- a ▬
- c ▭
- h

3
- p ▭
- l ▭
- a ▭
- n ▭
- k

4
- b ▭
- r ▭
- o ▭
- w ▭
- n

5
- p ▭
- e ▭
- a ▭
- r ▭
- l

6
- h ▭
- e ▭
- a ▭
- r ▭
- d

7
- r ▭
- e ▭
- l ▭
- a ▭
- y

EXAMPLE
- m ▭
- t ▭
- p ▭
- d ▭
- y ▬

8
- d ▭
- l ▭
- r ▭
- s ▭
- t ▭

9
- c ▭
- d ▭
- g ▭
- m ▭
- p ▭

10
- d ▭
- g ▭
- n ▭
- t ▭
- y ▭

11
- a ▭
- e ▭
- g ▭
- h ▭
- o ▭

12
- b ▭
- d ▭
- g ▭
- t ▭
- w ▭

13
- a ▭
- e ▭
- i ▭
- o ▭
- u ▭

14
- d ▭
- m ▭
- n ▭
- p ▭
- t

15
- d ▭
- l ▭
- m ▭
- s ▭
- t

EXAMPLE
- WD ▭
- BW ▭
- BY ▭
- DW ▬
- YB ▭

16
- CJ ▭
- JC ▭
- JD ▭
- DJ ▭
- EJ ▭

17
- ZN ▭
- ZY ▭
- ZM ▭
- XM ▭
- XY ▭

18
- JR ▭
- GJ ▭
- RN ▭
- OR ▭
- NR ▭

19
- VX ▭
- OX ▭
- PX ▭
- XO ▭
- XV ▭

20
- DU ▭
- FU ▭
- FW ▭
- UF ▭
- UD ▭

21
- SL ▭
- SM ▭
- KN ▭
- KL ▭
- KM ▭

22
- EI ▭
- IE ▭
- IF ▭
- KG ▭
- GK ▭

23
- a ▭
- b ▭
- c ▭
- d ▭
- e ▭

EXAMPLE
- He skis ▭
- skis so ▬
- so badly. ▭

24
- The hospital ▭
- hospital entrance ▭
- entrance is ▭
- is over ▭
- over there. ▭

25
- You really ▭
- really need ▭
- need to ▭
- to concentrate ▭
- concentrate today. ▭

26
- We meet ▭
- meet for ▭
- for lunch ▭
- lunch at ▭
- at noon. ▭

27
- Why is ▭
- is that ▭
- that parcel ▭
- parcel lying ▭
- lying there? ▭

28
- It is ▭
- is often ▭
- often cold ▭
- cold in ▭
- in April. ▭

29
- The window ▭
- window nearest ▭
- nearest Alice ▭
- Alice is ▭
- is open. ▭

30
- He never ▭
- never behaves ▭
- behaves well ▭
- well in ▭
- in class. ▭

31
- a ▭
- b ▭
- c ▭
- d ▭
- e ▭

EXAMPLE
- tiger ▭
- kitten ▬
- calf ▭
- bone ▭
- kennel ▭
- puppy ▬

32
- sturdy ▭
- fragile ▭
- glass ▭
- strong ▭
- steal ▭
- robot ▭

33
- congregation ▭
- altar ▭
- spire ▭
- ticket ▭
- audience ▭
- play ▭

34
- tool ▭
- bang ▭
- nail ▭
- crockery ▭
- cutlery ▭
- knife ▭

35
- petal ▭
- bee ▭
- flower ▭
- elephant ▭
- nose ▭
- tree ▭

36
- finished ▭
- continuous ▭
- end ▭
- intend ▭
- meddle ▭
- interval ▭

37
- palm ▭
- month ▭
- calendar ▭
- sultana ▭
- vine ▭
- wine ▭

38
- dustbin ▭
- accept ▭
- deny ▭
- spend ▭
- purse ▭
- coins ▭

PLEASE TURN OVER THE PAGE

EXAMPLE	39	40	41	42	43	44	45
WETS ☐	JMRE ☐	LEFT ☐	KHEW ☐	OATS ☐	UJOW ☐	TASK ☐	BKNVC ☐
VETS ☐	JMTD ☐	LESS ☐	KHDV ☐	OAST ☐	UJOZ ☐	VOLE ☐	BKNTC ☐
VEST ☐	JMTC ☐	PLUS ☐	KHDW ☐	MIST ☐	UJMW ☐	TILE ☐	DMPTE ☐
TEST ▬	NQXG ☐	PLUG ☐	EBXQ ☐	MATS ☐	SHUX ☐	RUSK ☐	DKPTE ☐
WEST ☐	NXQG ☐	PLUM ☐	EBBQ ☐	MAST ☐	SHMX ☐	TUSK ☐	DMPVE ☐

EXAMPLE	46	47	48
borrow ▬ purchase ☐	attack ☐ lose ☐	recollect ☐ remember ☐	stiff ☐ supple ☐
buy ☐ own ☐	fight ☐ retreat ☐	disperse ☐ forget ☐	flexible ☐ tight ☐
sell ☐ lend ▬	advance ☐ strike ☐	gather ☐ mislay ☐	nimble ☐ elastic ☐

49	50	51	52
improve ☐ clean ☐	cautious ☐ vicious ☐	fake ☐ gold ☐	celebrated ☐ unknown ☐
practise ☐ flawed ☐	slapdash ☐ careful ☐	real ☐ invaluable ☐	feasted ☐ famous ☐
perfect ☐ immaculate ☐	neat ☐ undiluted ☐	valuable ☐ genuine ☐	danced ☐ enjoyed ☐

EXAMPLE	53	54	55	56	57	58	59
6 ☐	36 ☐	54 ☐	0 ☐	12 ☐	17 ☐	10 ☐	4 ☐
7 ☐	58 ☐	56 ☐	1 ☐	16 ☐	18 ☐	11 ☐	6 ☐
8 ☐	74 ☐	72 ☐	2 ☐	30 ☐	19 ☐	12 ☐	8 ☐
9 ▬	78 ☐	81 ☐	3 ☐	31 ☐	20 ☐	14 ☐	12 ☐
10 ☐	104 ☐	108 ☐	4 ☐	32 ☐	24 ☐	15 ☐	14 ☐

EXAMPLE	60	61	62	63	64	65	66
fair ▬	cottage ☐	box ☐	destroy ☐	drop ☐	cloth ☐	bloom ☐	aid ☐
party ☐	house ☐	field ☐	howl ☐	crack ☐	bind ☐	clean ☐	save ☐
fete ☐	address ☐	mobile ☐	ruin ☐	rip ☐	veil ☐	rose ☐	bank ☐
festival ☐	town ☐	paddock ☐	tear ☐	shatter ☐	mask ☐	spray ☐	invest ☐
rave ☐	village ☐	ring ☐	scream ☐	spoil ☐	seek ☐	wedding ☐	preserve ☐

EXAMPLE	67	68	69	70	71	72	73
4 ☐	102 ☐	9 ☐	6 ☐	28 ☐	2 ☐	55 ☐	8 ☐
5 ☐	121 ☐	10 ☐	7 ☐	30 ☐	3 ☐	62 ☐	9 ☐
10 ☐	122 ☐	11 ☐	8 ☐	33 ☐	4 ☐	63 ☐	13 ☐
15 ▬	133 ☐	12 ☐	9 ☐	34 ☐	5 ☐	64 ▬	15 ☐
20 ☐	145 ☐	14 ☐	11 ☐	36 ☐	6 ☐	65 ☐	16 ☐

EXAMPLE	74	75	76	77	78	79	80
cream ☐	ship ☐	rots ☐	idea ☐	cared ☐	hers ☐	pray ☐	seat ☐
carat ☐	sing ☐	riot ☐	dear ☐	caned ☐	hear ☐	part ☐	sear ☐
camel ▬	spin ☐	trim ☐	teat ☐	candy ☐	hart ☐	pair ☐	soar ☐
racer ☐	shin ☐	trot ☐	tear ☐	dance ☐	they ☐	harp ☐	shoe ☐
trace ☐	ring ☐	torn ☐	tied ☐	farce ☐	tray ☐	rapt ☐	shot ☐

END OF TEST 4

Paper 3

In each sentence there is a word of **four** letters hidden between the end of one word and the beginning of the next.

Find the pair of words that contains the hidden word and mark your answer on the answer sheet.

Example

He skis so badly.

Answer

skis so (the hidden word is **kiss**)

QUESTION **1**

There is hair on your jacket.

QUESTION **2**

He loves his three white mice.

QUESTION **3**

It was quiet in the village.

QUESTION **4**

Make enough cakes for us all!

QUESTION **5**

Anna created an aromatic herb garden.

QUESTION **6**

Our relatives are away this week.

QUESTION **7**

Have you got your geometry set?

KEEP GOING

In these questions, find a letter that will complete the word in front of the brackets and begin the word after the brackets. You must use the **same** letter in **both** sets of brackets.

Example

tra (?) et
man (?) es

Answer

y (the four words are **tray, yet, many, yes**)

QUESTION **8**

hu (?) urn
ru (?) rag

QUESTION **9**

u (?) hip
ye (?) up

QUESTION **10**

ho (?) hite
blo (?) ig

QUESTION **11**

her (?) ath
sta (?) ugle

QUESTION **12**

to (?) dour
sol (?) mit

QUESTION **13**

car (?) arn
rod (?) asy

QUESTION **14**

pra (?) et
man (?) our

GO STRAIGHT ON

20

In these questions, letters represent numbers. Work out the answer to each sum, find its letter and mark it on the answer sheet.

Example

If   A=4,   B=3,   C=2,   D=6,   E=1,

what is the answer to this sum **as a letter**?

$$(B \times A) \div C = [?]$$

Answer

   D

QUESTION **15**

If   A=3,   B=24,   C=2,   D=16,   E=12,

what is the answer to this sum **as a letter**?

$$(B \div A) \times C = [?]$$

QUESTION **16**

If   A=16,   B=8,   C=2,   D=4,   E=10,

what is the answer to this sum **as a letter**?

$$(A \times C) \div B = [?]$$

QUESTION **17**

If   A=2,   B=8,   C=6,   D=4,   E=0,

what is the answer to this sum **as a letter**?

$$(C - A + D) \div A = [?]$$

QUESTION **18**

If   A=20,   B=4,   C=16,   D=2,   E=8,

what is the answer to this sum **as a letter**?

$$(C \div B) + (E \times D) = [?]$$

QUESTION **19**

If   A=3,   B=4,   C=9,   D=12,   E=2,

what is the answer to this sum **as a letter**?

$$(A \times D) \div C = [?]$$

QUESTION **20**

If   A=18,   B=4,   C=3,   D=9,   E=6,

what is the answer to this sum **as a letter**?

$$(A \div C) + (B \times C) = [?]$$

QUESTION **21**

If   A=4,   B=7,   C=9,   D=5,   E=3,

what is the answer to this sum **as a letter**?

$$(C + B + A) \div D = [?]$$

Read the following information, then work out the correct answer to the question and mark it on the answer sheet.

QUESTION **22**

Kate and her friends like to do Sudoku puzzles.
All the puzzles are the same level.
Manveer is the fastest. He does eight in one hour.
It takes Rashid two hours to do the same puzzles.
Kate does two more puzzles per hour than Rashid.

How long will it take Kate to do eighteen puzzles?

a. 1 hour

b. 2 hours

c. 3 hours

d. 4 hours

e. 90 minutes

KEEP GOING

GO STRAIGHT ON

21

Find **two** words, **one** from the top row and **one** from the bottom row, that are **closest in meaning**.

Mark **both** words on the answer sheet.

Example

      (scent glass fragrant)
      (bottle liquid odour)

Answer

      scent   odour

QUESTION **23**

(force make soldier)
(police power destroy)

QUESTION **24**

(region reign ruler)
(diameter line area)

QUESTION **25**

(play toil relax)
(football idle labour)

QUESTION **26**

(own mine gift)
(take possess receive)

QUESTION **27**

(freedom captivity prison)
(convict lock liberty)

QUESTION **28**

(sure uncertain left)
(right wrong doubtful)

QUESTION **29**

(cry apologise pardon)
(forgive laugh permit)

KEEP GOING

In each of the following sentences, **three letters next to each other** have been removed from the word in capitals.
These three letters make one correctly spelt word without changing their order.
Find the missing three letter word and mark it on the answer sheet.
The sentence must make sense.

Example

    The cock **CED** loudly every morning.

Answer

    ROW (The word in capitals is **CROWED**)

QUESTION **30**

The boy spread **DAM** jam on his toast.

QUESTION **31**

Is your **DESY** in the stars?

QUESTION **32**

The wedding cake was in three **RS.**

QUESTION **33**

Please tell me the **TH.**

QUESTION **34**

SM rose from the boiling pan.

QUESTION **35**

That is **PERAL** information.

QUESTION **36**

The boy's work was very **CRIVE**.

GO STRAIGHT ON

Each question below contains three pairs of words. Find the word that completes the last pair of words in the **same way** as the other two pairs.

Mark your answer on the answer sheet.

Example

(three   the)   (shame   she)
(bacon   [?])

Answer

ban

QUESTION **37**

(biscuit   sit)   (freesia   era)
(turret   [?])

QUESTION **38**

(window   wind)   (ducked   duck)
(danger   [?])

QUESTION **39**

(plant   apt)   (apron   ran)
(where   [?])

QUESTION **40**

(land   lane)   (fill   film)
(milk   [?])

QUESTION **41**

(tied   tried)   (pay   pray)
(bead   [?])

QUESTION **42**

(heater   hate)   (priest   pier)
(cloister   [?])

QUESTION **43**

(doomed   mood)   (earthy   tray)
(turtle   [?])

KEEP GOING

In the following questions, find **one** word from the top row and **one** word from the bottom row that will join together to form **one** correctly spelt new word.
The word from the top row always comes first.
Mark **both** words on the answer sheet.

Example

(he   she   we)
(am   at   are)

Answer

he   at   (the word is **heat**)

QUESTION **44**

(cot   since   fir)
(rely   age   try)

QUESTION **45**

(past   hum   man)
(our   try   edge)

QUESTION **46**

(ram   tomb   crumb)
(sack   tour   bled)

QUESTION **47**

(sow   reap   sew)
(apple   plum   pear)

QUESTION **48**

(comb   ram   sup)
(pert   bat   part)

QUESTION **49**

(at   port   dim)
(rate   tend   some)

QUESTION **50**

(ran   time   peas)
(able   side   sack)

QUESTION **51**

(mist   pan   poet)
(are   near   try)

GO STRAIGHT ON

23

In the following questions, find the number that will complete the sum correctly and mark it on the answer sheet.

Example

$$36 \div 3 = [\ ?\ ] \times 3$$

Answer

4

QUESTION **52**

$$17 + 8 = 125 \div [\ ?\ ]$$

QUESTION **53**

$$23 - 5 = [\ ?\ ] \times 2$$

QUESTION **54**

$$16 + 5 - 6 = 15 \div [\ ?\ ] + 10$$

QUESTION **55**

$$41 - 13 = 4 \times [\ ?\ ]$$

QUESTION **56**

$$6 \times 12 = 51 + [\ ?\ ]$$

QUESTION **57**

$$90 \div 15 = 2 \times [\ ?\ ]$$

QUESTION **58**

$$25 - 7 = 72 \div [\ ?\ ]$$

KEEP GOING

In the following questions, three of the five words are related in some way.

Find the **two** words that do not go with these three and mark them **both** on the answer sheet.

Example

carrot   turnip   mango   pea   apple

Answer

mango   apple

QUESTION **59**

kite   oval   rectangle   diamond   circle

QUESTION **60**

astonishment   wander   ramble   wonder   rove

QUESTION **61**

attain   reach   buy   achieve   purchase

QUESTION **62**

plateau   peak   top   level   summit

QUESTION **63**

clock   calendar   hourglass   watch   diary

QUESTION **64**

origin   terminus   end   finish   source

QUESTION **65**

singe   char   blow   burn   puff

QUESTION **66**

barometer   ruler   elements   weather   thermometer

GO STRAIGHT ON

Read the following information, then work out the correct answer to the question and mark it on the answer sheet.

QUESTION 67

In the sweet shop, the gobstoppers are two shelves beneath the bubblegum and one shelf above the chocolate bars.
The chews are one shelf above the gobstoppers.
The sherbet is one shelf below the bubblegum.

Which two items share a shelf?

a. chews and sherbet

b. bubblegum and sherbet

c. chocolate bars and sherbet

d. bubblegum and chews

e. gobstoppers and chocolate bars

GO STRAIGHT ON

A B C D E F G H I J K L M N O P Q R S T U V W X Y Z

The alphabet is here to help you with the following questions. Work out which pair of letters will come next in the series and mark your answer on the answer sheet.

Example

LX   MW   NV   OU   [?]

Answer

PT

QUESTION 68

PC   SE   VI   YO   BW   [?]

QUESTION 69

PB   NZ   LX   JV   HT   [?]

QUESTION 70

AL   BK   CJ   DI   EH   [?]

QUESTION 71

ZA   YB   XC   WD   VE   [?]

QUESTION 72

GB   ID   LG   PK   UP   [?]

QUESTION 73

AB   EC   ID   ME   QF   [?]

QUESTION 74

LB   OY   RV   US   XP   [?]

GO STRAIGHT ON

Three of these four words are written in number code.

The codes are **not** written in the same order as the words and one of the codes is missing.

SKIP   SIFT   SPIT   KISS

6211   1324   1254

Work out the correct code for each word and answer the following questions.

Mark the correct answer on the answer sheet.

QUESTION **75**

Which word has the number code **6211**?

QUESTION **76**

Find the code for the word **SKIP.**

QUESTION **77**

Find the code for the word **FIST.**

KEEP GOING

Three of these four words are written in number code.

The codes are **not** written in the same order as the words and one of the codes is missing.

DICE   TIDE   DIET   EDIT

1425   1432   5412

Work out the correct code for each word and answer the following questions.

Mark the correct answer on the answer sheet.

QUESTION **78**

Which word has the number code **2145**?

QUESTION **79**

Find the code for the word **ICED.**

QUESTION **80**

Find the code for the word **DIET.**

END OF TEST 3

26

Paper 4

In the following questions, take a letter from the first word and move it into the second word to form two new words.

All the other letters must stay in the same order and both new words must make sense.

Work out which letter moves and mark it on the answer sheet.

Example

> heart   camp

Answer

> **r**   (the two new words
> are **heat** and **cramp**)

QUESTION **1**

found   cell

QUESTION **2**

teach   later

QUESTION **3**

plank   span

QUESTION **4**

brown   door

QUESTION **5**

pearl   sill

QUESTION **6**

heard   sing

QUESTION **7**

relay   place

KEEP GOING

In these questions, find a letter that will complete the word in front of the brackets and begin the word after the brackets. You must use the **same** letter in **both** sets of brackets.

Example

> tra   (?)   et
> man   (?)   es

Answer

> **y**   (the four words are
> **tray, yet, many, yes**)

QUESTION **8**

pea   (?)   ow
mise   (?)   amp

QUESTION **9**

cla   (?)   oat
har   (?)   ine

QUESTION **10**

bra   (?)   ear
ha   (?)   ou

QUESTION **11**

din   (?)   arn
rat   (?)   go

QUESTION **12**

dra   (?)   arn
cur   (?)   ait

QUESTION **13**

und   (?)   il
sol   (?)   ver

QUESTION **14**

tra   (?)   art
har   (?)   oet

QUESTION **15**

die   (?)   uck
meri   (?)   ail

GO STRAIGHT ON

ABCDEFGHIJKLMNOPQRSTUVWXYZ

The alphabet is here to help you with the following questions.
Work out which pair of letters will come next in the sequence and mark your answer on the answer sheet.

Example

AZ is to BY
as
CX is to [?]

Answer

DW

QUESTION **16**

IO   is to   LR
as
AG   is to   [?]

QUESTION **17**

WL   is to   XF
as
YS   is to   [?]

QUESTION **18**

AJ   is to   EN
as
KN   is to   [?]

QUESTION **19**

PS   is to   MV
as
RU   is to   [?]

QUESTION **20**

CX   is to   DW
as
EV   is to   [?]

KEEP GOING

QUESTION **21**

HC   is to   DF
as
OJ   is to   [?]

QUESTION **22**

RN   is to   QM
as
JF   is to   [?]

Read the information below and work out which statement is true.
Mark its letter on the answer sheet.

QUESTION **23**

44 children took part in a swimming gala.
Rebecca came sixth.
She tied with four other children.

How many children did Rebecca beat?

a. 38

b. 35

c. 34

d. 37

e. 33

GO STRAIGHT ON

29

In each sentence there is a word of **four** letters hidden between the end of one word and the beginning of the next. Find the pair of words that contains the hidden word and mark your answer on the answer sheet.

Example

> He skis so badly.

Answer

> **skis so** (the hidden word is **kiss**)

QUESTION **24**

The hospital entrance is over there.

QUESTION **25**

You really need to concentrate today.

QUESTION **26**

We meet for lunch at noon.

QUESTION **27**

Why is that parcel lying there?

QUESTION **28**

It is often cold in April.

QUESTION **29**

The window nearest Alice is open.

QUESTION **30**

He never behaves well in class.

KEEP GOING

Read the information below and work out which statement is true.
Mark its letter on the answer sheet.

QUESTION **31**

Jasraj, Beth, Sophie and Oliver have pets.
All four children have goldfish.
Oliver and Sophie have dogs.
Beth has a Siamese.
Jasraj, Sophie and Oliver have gerbils.

Which of the following statements is true?

a. Jasraj has a cat.

b. Beth has a fish and a cat.

c. Sophie has a dog and a cat.

d. Jasraj hates hamsters.

e. All the children love gerbils.

In each of the following questions, there is the same relationship between the word outside the brackets and a word inside each set of brackets. Choose **two** words, one from each set of brackets, that complete the sentence in the best way.

Example

> **cat** is to
> (tiger   kitten   calf)
>
> as **dog** is to
> (bone   kennel   puppy)

Answer

> **kitten   puppy**

QUESTION **32**

frail is to
(sturdy   fragile   glass)

as **robust** is to
(strong   steal   robot)

GO STRAIGHT ON

QUESTION **33**

church is to
(congregation altar spire)

as **theatre** is to
(ticket audience play)

QUESTION **34**

hammer is to
(tool bang nail)

as **spoon** is to
(crockery cutlery knife)

QUESTION **35**

stem is to
(petal bee flower)

as **trunk** is to
(elephant nose tree)

QUESTION **36**

ceaseless is to
(finished continuous end)

as **interfere** is to
(intend meddle interval)

QUESTION **37**

date is to
(palm month calendar)

as **grape** is to
(sultana vine wine)

QUESTION **38**

refuse is to
(dustbin accept deny)

as **money** is to
(spend purse coins)

GO STRAIGHT ON

A B C D E F G H I J K L M N O P Q R S T U V W X Y Z

The alphabet is here to help you with the
following questions.
There is a different code for each question.
Find the correct answer and mark it on the
answer sheet.

Example

If the code for **HARD** is **IBSE**,
what does **UFTU** mean?

Answer

TEST

QUESTION **39**

If the code for **TRUE** is **RPSC**,
what is the code for **LOVE**?

QUESTION **40**

If the code for **GROW** is **EOMT**,
what does **NISJ** mean?

QUESTION **41**

If the code for **BAND** is **EDQG**,
what is the code for **HEAT**?

QUESTION **42**

If the code for **SHIP** is **TJLT**,
what does **NCVX** mean?

QUESTION **43**

If the code for **HUGE** is **IVHF**,
what is the code for **TINY**?

QUESTION **44**

If the code for **HUMP** is **ISPL**,
what does **USVG** mean?

QUESTION **45**

If the code for **GHOST** is **HGPRU**
what is the code for **CLOUD**?

GO STRAIGHT ON

In the following questions, find **two** words, one from each row, that are **most opposite in meaning**.

Example

      (borrow buy sell)
      (purchase own lend)

Answer
       borrow   lend

QUESTION **46**

(attack fight advance)
(lose retreat strike)

QUESTION **47**

(recollect disperse gather)
(remember forget mislay)

QUESTION **48**

(stiff flexible nimble)
(supple tight elastic)

QUESTION **49**

(improve practise perfect)
(clean flawed immaculate)

QUESTION **50**

(cautious slapdash neat)
(vicious careful undiluted)

QUESTION **51**

(fake real valuable)
(gold invaluable genuine)

QUESTION **52**

(celebrated feasted danced)
(unknown famous enjoyed)

KEEP GOING

In the following series, find the number which comes next in the most sensible way, and mark it on your answer sheet.

Example

      1   3   5   7   [?]

Answer

      9

QUESTION **53**

4   10   20   26   52   [?]

QUESTION **54**

1   2   6   12   36   [?]

QUESTION **55**

64   32   16   8   4   [?]

QUESTION **56**

3   6   7   14   15   [?]

QUESTION **57**

2   7   11   14   16   [?]

QUESTION **58**

3   4   7   8   11   [?]

QUESTION **59**

6   4   8   6   10   [?]

GO STRAIGHT ON

In each question there are two pairs of words. Only **one** of the answers will go equally well with **both** pairs of words.

Mark one word on the answer sheet.

Example

(just   reasonable)
(blonde   light)

Answer

fair

QUESTION **60**

(consider   discuss)
(place   residence)

QUESTION **61**

(enclosure   circle)
(call   phone)

QUESTION **62**

(damage   rip)
(weep   cry)

QUESTION **63**

(split   break)
(decode   decipher)

QUESTION **64**

(hide   cover)
(garment   scarf)

QUESTION **65**

(splash   shower)
(sprig   bouquet)

QUESTION **66**

(rescue   help)
(keep   reserve)

KEEP GOING

In the following questions, the three numbers in **each** group are related in the **same** way.

Find the number which belongs with the last group and mark it on the answer sheet.

Example

(2 [6] 3)   (4 [8] 2)   (5 [?] 3)

Answer

15

QUESTION **67**

(7 [43] 6)   (9 [73] 8)   (12 [?] 11)

QUESTION **68**

(8 [3] 2)   (14 [6] 2)   (22 [?] 2)

QUESTION **69**

(36 [5] 6)   (48 [7] 6)   (54 [?] 6)

QUESTION **70**

(12 [22] 2)   (8 [28] 4)   (7 [?] 5)

QUESTION **71**

(16 [8] 2)   (36 [4] 9)   (48 [?] 24)

QUESTION **72**

(9 [55] 6)   (8 [57] 7)   (7 [?] 9)

QUESTION **73**

(2 [6] 10)   (3 [7] 11)   (11 [?] 19)

GO STRAIGHT ON

The word in brackets in the top row has
been formed using the letters from the
two words on either side.
Find the missing word in the second row
that has been formed in the **same way**
and mark your answer on the sheet.

Example

          acre   (actor)   tore
          care   (?)   melt

Answer
                 camel

QUESTION **74**

tail   (line)   mane
hips   (?)   grin

QUESTION **75**

lead   (hand)   shin
moon   (?)   stir

QUESTION **76**

play   (meal)   game
trip   (?)   date

QUESTION **77**

treat   (greet)   green
fancy   (?)   cider

QUESTION **78**

marrow   (warn)   brown
breath   (?)   dusty

KEEP GOING

QUESTION **79**

creak   (lake)   tackle
tiara   (?)   happy

QUESTION **80**

hat   (then)   enemy
has   (?)   other

END OF TEST 4

ANSWERS

PAPER 1

1. rest rain
2. hear ten
3. par king
4. in vent
5. know ledge
6. part ridge
7. bat her
8. f
9. i
10. r
11. p
12. n
13. c
14. i
15. E
16. A
17. A
18. D
19. C
20. C
21. B
22. e
23. He ached
24. going riding
25. The picture
26. men decided
27. agreed it
28. her badge
29. dust under
30. Tom baked
31. under, beneath
32. attack, assault
33. murder, assassinate
34. gift, present
35. small, minute
36. taut, rigid
37. enigma, riddle
38. imitate, mimic
39. mad, insane
40. mend, repair
41. damp, moist
42. scorn, despise
43. serious, grave
44. frequently, often
45. hinder, impede
46. 8
47. 4
48. 5
49. 16
50. 2
51. 2
52. 2
53. d
54. RIM
55. HIM
56. ANT
57. ERA
58. OUR
59. ICE
60. ACT
61. deem
62. dock
63. bust
64. meet
65. lane
66. rain
67. try
68. AJ
69. WA
70. YN
71. ZA
72. KE
73. YA
74. WI
75. FAST
76. 4362
77. 1652
78. LOOK
79. 1254
80. 1433

PAPER 2

1. g
2. w
3. m
4. r
5. b
6. w
7. t
8. b
9. c
10. b
11. a
12. l
13. e
14. c
15. DI
16. KP
17. RM
18. CA
19. QA
20. ZY
21. WP
22. E
23. absent, present
24. voluntary, compulsory
25. eager, reluctant
26. wealthy, impoverished
27. commence, cease
28. deteriorate, improve
29. folly, wisdom
30. extravagant, frugal
31. 36
32. 21
33. 18
34. 1
35. 33
36. 240
37. 25
38. pretty petals
39. boxer anticipated
40. foreman yelled
41. office downstairs
42. Each entrance
43. hair is
44. party really
45. b
46. pacify, annoy
47. bean, leaf
48. water, food
49. dawn, dusk
50. sit, lie
51. foundations, roots
52. time, direction
53. PGOIB
54. POINT
55. UKOIX
56. SHUT
57. USVV
58. PAGE
59. TFLZL
60. rule
61. charge
62. draw
63. contest
64. trip
65. dash
66. blooms
67. 5
68. 54
69. 20
70. 90
71. 83
72. 33
73. 34
74. 15
75. balm
76. moan
77. form
78. meaty
79. urn
80. sate

PAPER 3

1. hair on
2. white mice
3. the village
4. Make enough
5. Anna created
6. are away
7. your geometry
8. b
9. s
10. w
11. b
12. o
13. e
14. y
15. D
16. D
17. D
18. A
19. B
20. A
21. A
22. c
23. force, power
24. region, area
25. toil, labour
26. own, possess
27. freedom, liberty
28. uncertain, doubtful
29. pardon, forgive
30. SON
31. TIN
32. TIE
33. RUT
34. TEA
35. SON
36. EAT
37. rut
38. rang
39. ewe
40. mill
41. bread
42. coil
43. true
44. since   rely
45. hum   our
46. ram   bled
47. reap   pear
48. ram   part
49. at   tend
50. ran   sack
51. pan   try
52. 5
53. 9
54. 3
55. 7
56. 21
57. 3
58. 4
59. oval, circle
60. astonishment, wonder
61. buy, purchase
62. plateau, level
63. calendar, diary
64. origin, source
65. blow, puff
66. elements, weather
67. a
68. EG
69. FR
70. FG
71. UF
72. AV
73. UG
74. AM
75. KISS
76. 1623
77. 5214
78. EDIT
79. 4321
80. 1425

PAPER 4

1. o
2. t
3. k
4. n
5. p
6. e
7. a
8. r
9. m
10. y
11. e
12. b
13. o
14. p
15. t
16. DJ
17. ZM
18. OR
19. OX
20. FU
21. KM
22. IE
23. c
24. hospital entrance
25. you really
26. lunch at
27. parcel lying
28. is often
29. window nearest
30. never behaves
31. b
32. fragile, strong
33. congregation, audience
34. tool, cutlery
35. flower, tree
36. continuous, meddle
37. palm, vine
38. dustbin, purse
39. JMTC
40. PLUM
41. KHDW
42. MAST
43. UJOZ
44. TUSK
45. DKPTE
46. advance, retreat
47. recollect, forget
48. stiff, supple
49. perfect, flawed
50. slapdash, careful
51. fake, genuine
52. celebrated, unknown
53. 58
54. 72
55. 2
56. 30
57. 17
58. 12
59. 8
60. address
61. ring
62. tear
63. crack
64. veil
65. spray
66. save
67. 133
68. 10
69. 8
70. 30
71. 2
72. 64
73. 15
74. spin
75. torn
76. tear
77. candy
78. tray
79. pray
80. shot